Contents

S0-BDP-224

Special Features

Features

Bugs in the Garden

Written by Cory Winesap

This is a beetle.
It is in the garden.

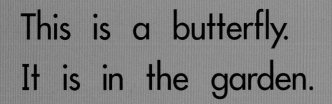

This is a butterfly.
It is in the garden.

This is a caterpillar.
It is in the garden.

This is a praying mantis.
It is in the garden.

This is a spider.
It is in the garden.

This is a bee.
It is in the garden.

This is a grasshopper.
It is in the garden.

Safari WORD POWER

 Aa

 Bb

 Cc

 Dd

Ee

Ff

Gg

Hh

Ii

 Zz

 Yy

 Xx

 Ww

 Vv

 Uu

 Tt

 Ss

 Rr

the   It   in   is   a   me   This

Find –
a in is It
me the This

 Jj Kk Ll Mm Nn Oo Pp Qq

Give Me a Hug

Written by Josephine Selwyn

Illustrated by Jim Storey

Bug, Bug,
Inside the mug.

Give me a hug,
Little bug.

Not on my nose,
Not on my toes.

Give me a hug,
Little bug.

bug
dug
hug
mug
plug
rug
slug
snug
bug
dug
hug
mug
plug
rug
slug
snug
bug
dug
hug
mug

I Live in the Garden

Written by Monique Martin
Illustrated by Fraser Williamson

I live in the garden.
I fly to the red flower.

I fly to the yellow flower
and the orange flower.

I fly to the pink flower
and the purple flower.

I live in the garden.

The Bug Race

Written by Sonny Reuben

Illustrated by Peter Campbell

Beetle

Caterpillar

Centipede

Earwig

Caterpillar

I will run fast.

I will win the race.

Beetle

I will run fast.

I will win the race.

Earwig

I will run fast.

I will win the race.

Centipede

I will run fast.

I will win the race.

 ## Caterpillar
Puff, puff, puff.
I will not win the race.

 ## Beetle
Puff, puff, puff.
I will not win the race.

 ## Earwig
Puff, puff, puff.
I will not win the race.

Centipede

I will win the race!

I will win the race!

Grasshopper Green

Written by Michele Ashley

Grasshopper, grasshopper,
Grasshopper green,
Looks just like
A long string bean.
Grasshopper, grasshopper,
Grasshopper green.

readingsafari.com

Check out these Safari magazines, too!

Have your say -

e-mail your Safari Tour Guide at
tourguide@readingsafari.com

Safari Tour Guide,

 40

I wrote a story about a big caterpillar.
Do you want me to send it to you?

Sara Woods (6)

Find some fun things to do!

Go to –
http://www.readingsafari.com

Safari *Superstar*

Name – Bumblebee

Birthday – July 5

Find out more about this Safari Superstar at
http://www.readingsafari.com